of co-ordination
is both valuable and
important to a child's later
development, and this is found,
for instance, in *Finger Rhymes*,
the first book of the eight book series.

This series provides an enjoyable intro-
duction to poetry, music and dance for
every young child. Most books of this
type have only a few rhymes for each
age group, whereas each book of this
series is intended for a particular age
group. There is a strong teaching sequence
in the selection of rhymes, from the
first simple ways of winning the child's
interest by toe tapping and palm
tickling jingles, through practice in
numbers, memory and pronunciation,
to combining sound, action and
words. For the first time young
children can learn rhymes
in a sequ
related

Contents

page

LEARNING WITH TRADITIONAL RHYMES

Skipping Rhymes

by **DOROTHY, ALISON** and **CAROLINE TAYLOR**
with illustrations by
BRIAN PRICE THOMAS
and photographs by **JOHN MOYES**

Ladybird Books Loughborough

Here are some skips you can do by yourself. Start by skipping slowly to the chant, then gradually increase the speed of your skipping and chanting.

Salt, mustard, vinegar, pepper,
Salt, mustard, vinegar, pepper, etc.

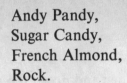

Andy Pandy,
Sugar Candy,
French Almond,
Rock.

Apple tree, pear tree, plum tree pie,
How many children before I die?
One, two, three, four, five, etc.

A for Apple,
B for Boy,
C for Cat,
D for Donkey, etc.

Skip until the point when, in thinking hard for a word, the fluency or rhythm is lost.

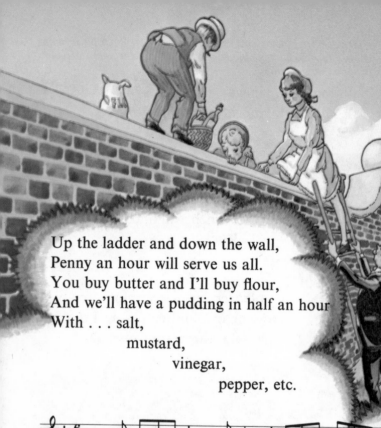

Up the ladder and down the wall,
Penny an hour will serve us all.
You buy butter and I'll buy flour,
And we'll have a pudding in half an hour
With . . . salt,
                mustard,
                        vinegar,
                                pepper, etc.

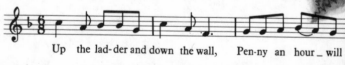

Up the lad-der and down the wall, Pen-ny an hour _ will

serve us all. You buy but-ter and I'll buy flour, And

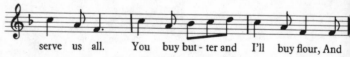

we'll have a pud-ding in half an hour *(Chant)*: With salt, mustard, etc.

Mrs Brown went to town
Riding on a pony.
When she came back
She lost her hat
And called on Miss Maloney.

M - rs Brown went to town— Ri - ding on a po - ny. When
she came back She lost her hat And called on Miss Ma - lo - ney.

Cups and saucers,
Plates and dishes,
My old man wears
Calico breeches.

8

Early in the morning at half past eight,
I heard the postman knocking at the gate.
Postman, postman, drop your letter,
Lady, lady, pick it up.
I spy a lark, shining in the dark,
Echo, echo, G.O. stands for GO!

Half a pound of tuppenny rice,

Half a pound of treacle.

Mix it up and make it nice,

Pop goes the Weasel!

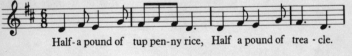

Half-a pound of tup pen-ny rice, Half a pound of trea-cle.

Mix it up and make it nice, Pop goes the Wea-sel.

These are skips you can do either by yourself or with two people turning the rope for you.

Blackcurrant, redcurrant, raspberry tart,
Tell me the name of your sweetheart,
A.B.C.D.E., etc.

The letter of the alphabet on which you trip or stumble is the beginning letter of your sweetheart's name. Or, in the rhyme below, the name of your future husband or wife.

Ipsey, Pipsey,
Tell me true,
Who shall I be married to?
A.B.C.D.E., etc.

For these skips you will need at least three (two rope turners and a skipper).

I am a girl guide dressed in blue,
These are the actions I must do,
Salute to the Captain, bow to the Queen,
Twist right round and count fifteen.
One, two, three, etc.

14

Bluebells, cockle shells,
Eavy, Ivy, OVER.
This is how the alphabet goes,
A.B.C., etc.

*Sway rope gently until the word OVER when the rope is
turned completely over, this action being continued to the end.*

*Two players turn
the rope as another
skips. At 'wibble, wobble,
wibble, wobble,' they wiggle
the rope from side to side.
At 'turn them over',
they turn the rope quickly
as skipper jumps. At
'turn him out', the skipper
runs out of the rope.*

Jelly on a plate,
Jelly on a plate,
Wibble, wobble, wibble, wobble,
Jelly on a plate.

Sausages in the pan,
Sausages in the pan,
Turn them over, turn them over,
Sausages in the pan.

Ghostie in the house,
Ghostie in the house,
Turn him out, turn him out,
Ghostie in the house.

On a mountain stands a lady,
Who she is I do not know,
All she wants is gold and silver,
All she wants is a nice young man.

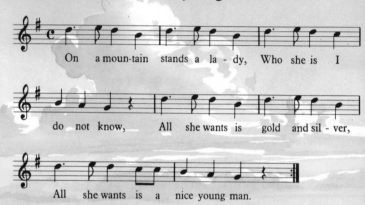

On a moun-tain stands a la - dy, Who she is I
do not know, All she wants is gold and sil - ver,
All she wants is a nice young man.

Teddy bear, teddy bear, turn around,
Teddy bear, teddy bear, touch the ground.
Teddy bear, teddy bear, climb upstairs,
Teddy bear, teddy bear, say your prayers.
Teddy bear, teddy bear, turn off the light,
Teddy bear, teddy bear, say goodnight.

Actions to this rhyme are self-evident.

At least four people
stand in line ready to
run in to the rope one
after the other without a
pause. When everyone has
had a turn to skip down, the
sequence begins again with up
to Mississippi.

For 'down', skip and go down.
On 'up' push both arms high in air.

Down to Mississippi,
If you miss a loop you're out!

Up to Mississippi,
If you miss a loop you're out!

Hop to Mississippi, etc.

Clap to Mississippi, etc.

One hand behind your back to Mississippi, etc.

Two hands behind your back to Mississippi, etc.

High, low,
Medium, slow,
Dolly, Rocker,
Pepper.

Actions: Two people hold the rope.
First person enters the rope; then the two people turning the
rope increase speed gradually until the word 'pepper', when
the rope is turned at a fast speed.
If skipper makes a mistake in the course of this rhyme, he or
she must pay a forfeit, eg:
If out on 'low' – she must skip 10 low skips (rope holders
squatting down low.)

If out on 'high' – the rope is turned as high as possible, skipper does 10 high skips.
If out on 'medium' – 10 skips at normal position.
If out on 'slow' – 10 skips slow.
If out on 'Dolly' – 10 skips whilst turning round, eyes shut.
If out on 'rocker' – 10 skips whilst rope is swayed from side to side.
If out on 'pepper' – 10 very fast skips.

Bumper car, bumper car,
Number twenty-eight
Went round the corner
And put on his brakes.

Two children turn the rope, while another player jumps from side to side moving in a forward direction. At 'went round the corner' the skipper goes round the back of one of the rope holders and on 'put on his brakes' finishes with feet astride the rope.

Cowboy Joe from Mexico,
Hands up, stick'em up,
Drop your guns and pick 'em up.

One skipper after the other runs in to the rope, alternately jumping under and over it.

Kings and Queens,
And partners two,
All dressed up
In royal blue.
Stand at ease,
Bend your knees,
Salute to the east
And bow to the west.

Actions to this rhyme are self-evident.

The wind, the wind, the wind blows high,
The rain comes falling from the sky.
She is handsome, she is pretty,
She is the girl of London city.
She goes a-courting one, two, three,
Please will you tell me who is he?
. . . . . says he loves her.
All the boys are fighting for her.
Let them all say what they will
. . . . . loves her still.

*The rope is turned by two children throughout the game.
Everyone sings the song after choosing a solo skipper. At the
appropriate time, the name of the skipper's boyfriend is loudly
sung. The game is then repeated to give each player a turn.*

Ci - ty.___ She goes a - Court - ing___ one, two,
for her.___ Let them___ all say___ what they

three, Please will you tell me Who is he?
will ------------------- Loves her still.

Down by the river,
He sat me on his knee.
He said 'My ducky darling,
Won't you marry me?'
Yes, no, yes, no, . . .

*Continue chanting yes, no, until a mistake is made. If the
skipper lands on 'no', then she is out. If she lands on 'yes',
then the following questions are asked:*

How many times did he kiss me?
One, two, three, etc.
When shall I marry?
January, February, March, etc.
What is the first letter of my husband's name?
A.B.C.D., etc.
What is he?
Tinker, tailor, soldier, sailor.

Up the ladder,
Down the ladder,
One, one, one.

Up the ladder,
Down the ladder,
Two, two, two.

*Two people hold the rope while
two players skip. The rope is
turned as the rhyme is chanted,
and the two players jump along
the rope from end to end
facing opposite directions.*

31

SKIPPING WITH LOTS OF FRIENDS

You will need a longer rope for these games.

All in together girls,
Never mind the weather girls,
When I call your birthday
Please run out.
January, February, March, etc.
(or January 1st, 2nd, 3rd, etc.)

Each child stands one behind the other in the skipping space, all facing in the same direction.

33

Vote, vote, vote for little . . . . .
In comes . . . . . at the door.
She is the one that we want,
And we don't want . . . . . any more.
Shut the door – BANG.

This is another rhyme where the first named player is joined by a second. The first one runs out and the second player starts the game again.

Every morning at eight o'clock,
You all may hear the postman knock,
1, 2, 3, 4, there goes . . . . .

In this game, everyone stands in the skipping space as before, except *for one boy or girl who takes the place of the one who is chosen to run out. (The rope turners may take turns to choose who should run out.)*

Chase the Fox (or 'Follow my Leader')

The leader runs through the rope as it is turned towards her or him, and the rest of the line follows suit.
The leader runs back through the rope as it is turned away from her or him. The others follow suit.
The leader runs in and jumps once. The others follow suit. Then the leader jumps twice, three times, four times, etc., each time followed by the rest of the children.

There are two chants for this game:

Fairies and Witches.

If you trip or stand on the rope, you are out. Tripping on the rope means you are a 'fairy', and you go behind one rope-holder. Standing on the rope means you are a 'witch', and you go behind the other rope-holder. The longest line wins.

I love coffee,
And Billy loves tea.

NUMBERS

1.
1, 2.
1, 2, 3.
1, 2, 3, 4.

One skipper after another jumps into the rope, the first one jumping once, the second, twice, the third, three times, and so on.

House to let,
Enquire within,
When I go out
Mrs . . . . comes in.

This time a line of children waits to run in, each in turn. The skipper chants the rhyme alone and chooses the one who is to follow her.

39

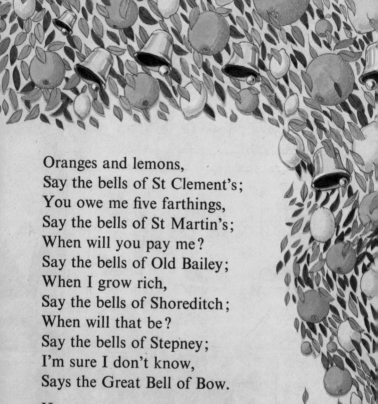

Oranges and lemons,
Say the bells of St Clement's;
You owe me five farthings,
Say the bells of St Martin's;
When will you pay me?
Say the bells of Old Bailey;
When I grow rich,
Say the bells of Shoreditch;
When will that be?
Say the bells of Stepney;
I'm sure I don't know,
Says the Great Bell of Bow.

Here comes a candle to light you to bed;
Here comes a chopper to chop off your head;
The last, last, last, last man's head.

*The rope is held by two players and the others skip through
the rope in turn. When a mistake is made the skipper whispers
her choice, either 'Oranges' or 'Lemons' (as in the singing
game), and makes a tail. A tug of war takes place when all
are out.*

Or-ang-es and lem-ons, Say the bells of St Cle-ment's; You

owe me five farth-ings, Say the bells of St Mar-tin's.

When will you pay me? Say the bells of Old Bai-ley;

When I grow rich Say the bells of Shore-ditch; When will that

be? Say the bells of Step-ney; I'm sure I don't know, Says the

Great Bell of Bow. *(Chant):* Here comes a candle etc.

My best friend is   . . . . (full name)
We've been friends for . . . . . years.
We've fallen out . . . . . times.

One skipper in the rope is joined by another whom he or she has named. At 'we've fallen out', first skipper skips out.

Suzy's in the kitchen,
Doing a bit of stitching,
In comes ..... and knocks her out!

The actions for this are the same as for 'My Best Friend'.

Someone's under the bed.
Whoever can it be?
For he's a jolly good fellow,
Call in . . . .(full name)
. . . . . (first name) lights a candle,
Then she sees a ghost,
Run out, run out,
Before you get a clout.

The two turning the rope shout the name of their chosen player.

FRENCH SKIPPING

You will need a length of narrow elastic, 3 yards long (2.75 metres). Tie a knot to join the two ends together.

Two children act as holders and stand facing each other inside the elastic with legs slightly apart. The elastic should be at ankle level and fairly taut.

If you want to play this game when you are by yourself use two chairs as elastic holders.

The holders remain in position while the skipper goes through a series of skipping movements. If he or she makes a mistake,

he or she takes the place of one of the holders whose turn it now is to be the skipper. When retaking a turn you start with the movement where the mistake was made.

The following words are frequently used:

INS
the skipper's feet
should look
like this:

ONS
like this:

OUTS
like this:

diagram (a)

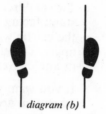

diagram (b)

diagram (c)

THE GAME

Movement 1 INS and OUTS

Starting in the
'OUTS' position
(diagram c), jump in and
out to the count of seven,
i.e. IN, OUT, IN, OUT,
IN, OUT, IN.

Movement 2 ONS

Start with feet
in the 'INS' position.
Jump ON (diagram b).
Jump IN (diagram a).
Jump ON again.
Jump OUT.

Movement 3   DIAMONDS

Make a diamond shape with the elastic as shown right.

Jump IN.

Make the diamond shape again.
Jump OUT.

Make another diamond shape.
Jump ON.

Movement 4   UNDERS and OVERS

Stand with one foot UNDER the elastic and the other foot OVER the same piece of elastic (fig 1).

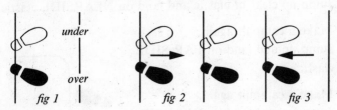

Jump to the other side of the elastic to land in the same position (fig 2).

Finally, jump backwards, finishing in starting position (fig 3).

Movement 5 JUMPS

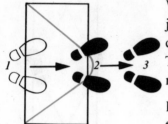

With both feet UNDER elastic jump on to far-side elastic, taking care to pull elastic with you. Then jump forward again, releasing the elastic as you do so.

Repeat this movement back the opposite way.

Movement 6 CATAPULTS

With your foot draw the far-side elastic towards you, under the nearside strand and hold down with both feet as shown below.

Jump up clear of elastic and land on NEARSIDE elastic.

Make a catapult again.
Jump up and land on FAR-SIDE
elastic.

Make a catapult again.
Jump up and land on NEARSIDE,
                    FAR-SIDE,
                    NEARSIDE.

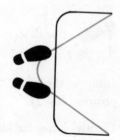

Movement 7 SWIZZLES

Start in OUT position but with feet close together like this:

Pivot anti-clockwise to face in the opposite direction, which twists elastic into an 'S' shape.

Jump IN.
Make 'S' again.
Jump OUT.
Make 'S' again.
Jump ON.

When you have completed all seven movements with elastic at ankle level you can repeat the sequence at calf level and then knee level.

See what different movements you can now make up for yourself.

•❊O❊•